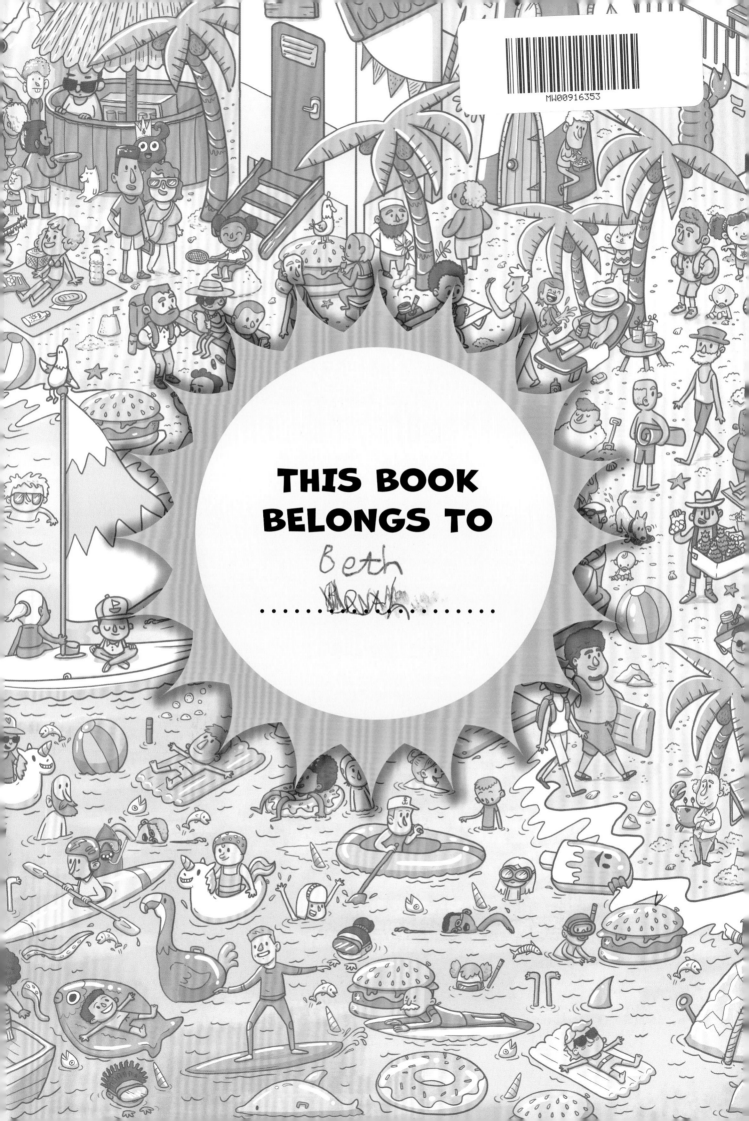

**THIS BOOK BELONGS TO**

Beth

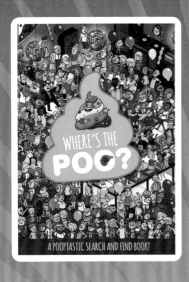

A POOPTASTIC SEARCH AND FIND BOOK!

# LOOK OUT FOR MORE POOP-TASTIC BOOKS IN THIS RANGE:

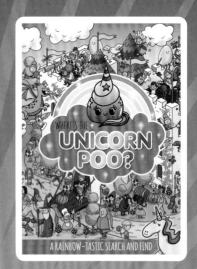

A RAINBOW-TASTIC SEARCH AND FIND

A DINO-TASTIC SEARCH AND FIND

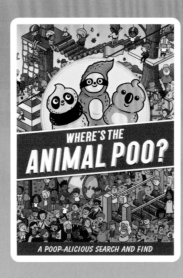

A POOP-ALICIOUS SEARCH AND FIND

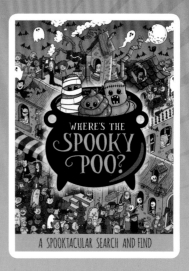

A SPOOKTACULAR SEARCH AND FIND

ON YOUR MARKS, GET SET, SEARCH!

A BRRRRR-illiant Search and Find

A SWASHBUCKLING SEARCH AND FIND

AN OUT-OF-THIS-WORLD SEARCH AND FIND

A CHRISTMAS SEARCH AND FIND

# WHERE'S THE HOLIDAY POO?

ORCHARD

# MEET THE POOS

School's out and the holiday poos are on the loose ...

The holiday poos have packed their suitcases and are off to find sunshine, snow and adventure! Can you spot them as they journey around the globe?

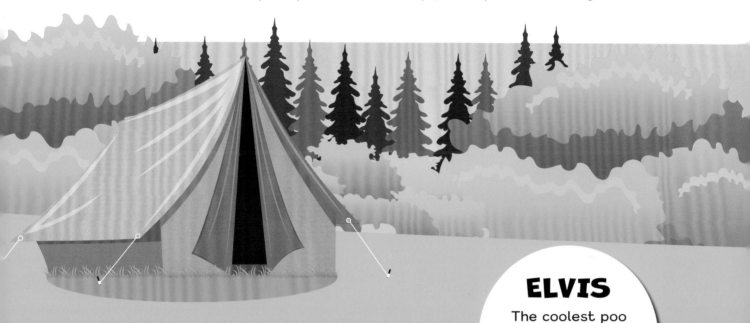

## ELVIS

The coolest poo in the crew, Elvis never forgets to pack his shades so he can enjoy the sunshine!

## BOBBI

The oldest of the group, Bobbi loves to go sightseeing. Unfortunately, she always seems to get lost!

**QUEENIE**

Say cheese! This is the Selfie Queen. She loves to snap photos when on holiday!

**STU**

The swimming poo is always messing around in the ocean. Let's see if he sinks or floats!

**DUCKIE**

Known as the chill poo, Duckie's ideal holiday involves relaxing and floating in the pool.

**ROO**

This kangaroo poo from down under is always hopping about. Can you find him hiding in one of the scenes?

# TAKE-OFF TIME

The holiday poos have arrived at the airport ready for the trip of a lifetime! Can you find them hiding before they board their plane?

# THE GREAT WALL

The poos are leaving their mark at this historic Chinese landmark. Can you spot Elvis and his crew?

# POO BARBECUE

Stu loves to get in touch with nature when he goes on holiday. Can you see him at this summer campsite?

# ARCTIC ANTICS

Pack your hats and gloves – the holiday poos are heading to the Arctic. Look for them sliding on the ice!

# KANGAPOOS

The poo gang love playing with boomerangs! Can you spot them bouncing around Sydney Harbour?

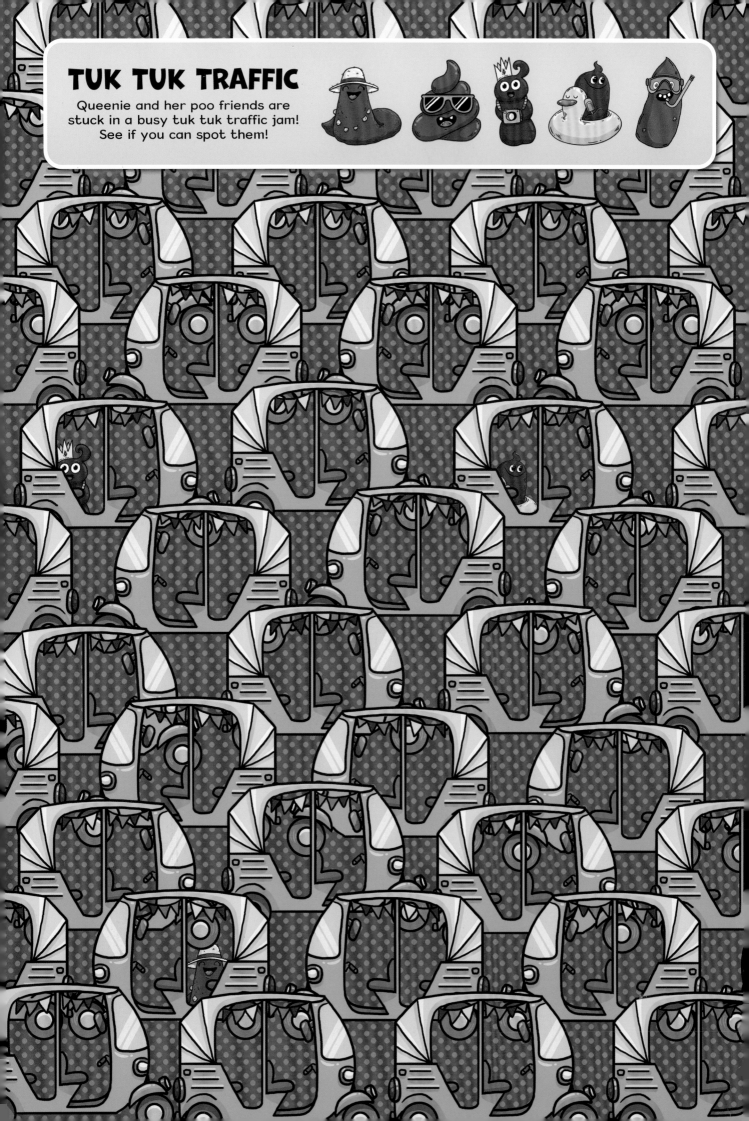

# TUK TUK TRAFFIC

Queenie and her poo friends are stuck in a busy tuk tuk traffic jam! See if you can spot them!

# BUSY BAZAAR

Bobbi is visiting an Indian market with her friends but she forgot her map. Can you spot the lost poos?

# JAPANESE GARDEN

The poos are in Japan, enjoying the koi ponds and beautiful gardens. See if you can find them among the cherry blossoms.

# DROPPING ANCHOR

The holiday poos are sailing out to their next destination. Can you find them bobbing on the waves?

**ODD ONE OUT!**
One of these ships is not like the others. Can you spot it?

# BEACH BUMS

Ah, the beach! Salt in the air, fish in the sea and ... poo in the sand? Quick, find the poos before someone steps on one of them!

# SUNNY SAFARI

The holiday poos are on safari! Can you find them touring this African nature reserve?

# PACK YOUR BAGS!

Queenie may have packed a bit too much luggage... Can you find her and the other poos among the suitcases?

# IN THE CANAL

The poos have dropped down to the Netherlands to float along the canal. But where are Duckie and his friends?

# WEE, MONSIEUR!

Something is stinking up the city of love. It's the holiday poos! Can you find them hiding in Paris?

# ANSWERS

Now try and find the extra
items hidden in each scene.

## TAKE-OFF TIME

1. Eight babies ☐

2. Four conveyor belts ☐

3. A muffin ☐

4. Three water bottles ☐

5. Four newspapers ☐

6. A goatee ☐

7. Five luggage tags ☐

8. Two Hawaiian shirts ☐

9. A neck pillow ☐

10. Two rolled-up mats ☐

## THE GREAT WALL

1. Seven lanterns ☐

2. A rabbit ☐

3. Seven cameras ☐

4. Eight birds ☐

5. Eight fortune cookies ☐

6. Three water bottles ☐

7. A purple flag ☐

8. Three pairs of yellow trousers ☐

9. An ice cream cone ☐

10. Someone picking their nose! ☐

## POO BARBECUE

1. Two kites
2. Six badminton rackets
3. Four bags of marshmallows
4. A bear
5. Two flippers
6. A blow-up mattress
7. Two rolls of toilet paper
8. Three wedges of cheese
9. A big hotdog
10. A pair of underwear

## ARCTIC ANTICS

1. A fishing rod
2. Three walruses
3. A photographer
4. Three arrows
5. A snowman
6. Nine penguin eggs
7. A red bauble
8. An owl
9. Five scuba divers
10. Six woolly hats

## KANGAPOOS

1. Two boomerangs ☐
2. An alligator ☐
3. Two surfboards ☐
4. Eight trees ☐
5. Two butterflies ☐
6. Two dogs ☐
7. A life-float ☐
8. Two boxing gloves ☐
9. A body-warmer jacket ☐
10. A taxi ☐

## TUK TUK TRAFFIC

## BUSY BAZAAR

1. Seven pots ☐
2. A sitar ☐
3. Three monkeys ☐
4. Eleven chillies ☐
5. Two snakes ☐
6. Four mopeds ☐
7. Two rickshaws ☐
8. Four carrots ☐
9. A scooter ☐
10. Four pineapples ☐

## JAPANESE GARDEN

1. Fourteen fish ☐
2. Two women holding two ice creams ☐
3. Twelve circular stones ☐
4. A brown package ☐
5. Seventeen trees ☐
6. A yellow phone ☐
7. Fourteen lily pads ☐
8. Two birds ☐
9. An orange kimono ☐
10. Two bonsai trees ☐

Did you find me? If you're stuck, try looking again at Beach Bums.

## DROPPING ANCHOR

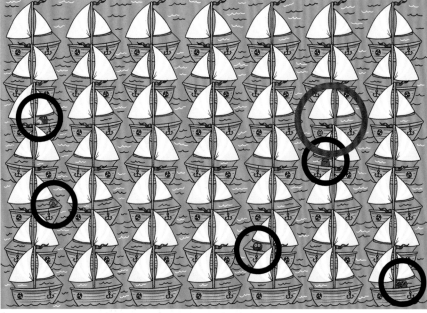

## BEACH BUMS

1. An octopus ☐
2. Seven palm trees ☐
3. A blue guitar ☐
4. Sixteen sandcastles ☐
5. A buoy ☐
6. Two surfers ☐
7. A girl doing a cannonball ☐
8. Three donuts ☐
9. A starfish balloon ☐
10. A pedalo ☐

## SUNNY SAFARI

1. Six zebras ☐

2. Seven giraffes ☐

3. Four warthogs ☐

4. Six wildebeests ☐

5. Three baby elephants ☐

6. Six hyenas ☐

7. Three rhinos ☐

8. Five frogs ☐

9. Four lions ☐

10. Five gazelles ☐

## PACK YOUR BAGS!

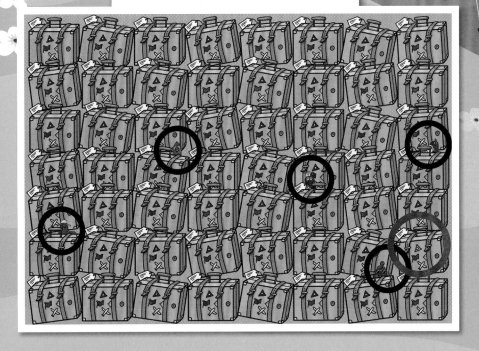

## ON THE CANAL

1. A fried egg ☐
2. Two satellite dishes ☐
3. A seahorse ☐
4. Five rabbits ☐
5. A goldfish ☐
6. Four mice ☐
7. Three life jackets ☐
8. A banana peel ☐
9. Seven plant pots ☐
10. A unicycle ☐

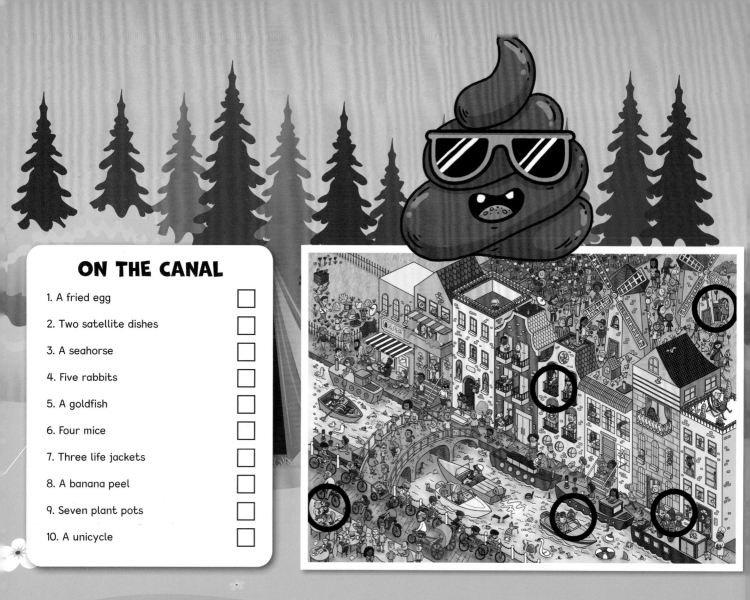

## WEE, MONSIEUR!

1. Two lamps ☐
2. Eight cyclists ☐
3. A speaker ☐
4. Two poodles ☐
5. A slice of watermelon ☐
6. The Eiffel Tower ☐
7. A drain ☐
8. Twenty-nine pigeons ☐
9. Three croissants ☐
10. A pair of red headphones ☐

ORCHARD BOOKS
First published in Great Britain in 2023 by Hodder & Stoughton Ltd © 2023 Hodder & Stoughton Ltd
Illustrations by Dynamo Limited        Additional images © Shutterstock
A CIP catalogue record for this book is available from the British Library
ISBN 978 1 40836 439 0        Printed and bound in China        3 5 7 9 10 8 6 4 2

Orchard Books, an imprint of Hachette Children's Group
Part of Hodder & Stoughton Ltd, Carmelite House, 50 Victoria Embankment, London, EC4Y 0DZ
An Hachette UK Company        www.hachette.co.uk        www.hachettechildrens.co.uk

FSC
www.fsc.org
MIX
Paper from
responsible sources
FSC® C169965